Why I'm Proud to Be an AMERICAN

From the hearts of America's kids

edited by Peggy Gavan

Troll

ISBN 0-8167-7500-1

Printed in Canada.

10 9 8 7 6 5 4 3 2 1

Why are you proud to be an American kid?

That's the question we asked kids across America, from sea to shining sea, in our *Why I'm Proud to Be an American* contest. And the mail came pouring in from every state and U.S. territory! Thousands of students in grades PreK–9 sent us their patriotic prose, poetry, and pictures on topics such as justice and freedom, the American flag, the Fourth of July, and the heroes of September 11.

The very best submissions—creative, inspiring, and thoughtful—were compiled and put into this book, along with each winner's name, grade, hometown, and state.

Thank you to every student who entered the contest. You are all winners, because you are all great American kids! Finally, thank you to all the teachers who encouraged their students and helped inspire them to be so proud of our nation.

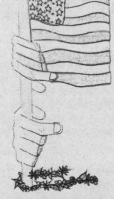

Brittany D., Grade 8, Battle Ground, Washington

Unforgettable! Spectacular! Amazing!

Perfect
Radical
Oh, take me out to the ball game
United forever
Dude, it's cool

Terrific
Oh say, can you see

Best place to be
Everyone gets along

America the beautiful
Nobody wants to leave

All men and women are equal
Mighty and strong
Education is available to everyone
Rights are respected
Individuality
Courageous
All people can do what they want
Nation is free

Kids have rights
It is awesome
Dull? No way!

Michaela O., Grade 4, Hansen, Massachusetts

I'm proud to be a:
  baseball-plAying
            MoM-loving
    Dad-wrEstling
      book-Reading
          Ice-cream-eating
        sCout-attending
      flag-wAving
  church-goiNg kid!

W.J. M., Grade 2, Marshville, North Carolina

A is for America.
M is for our marvelous land "from sea to shining sea."
E is for everyone, whoever we may be.
R is for red, white, and blue, the colors of our flag.
I is for the incredible states we live in.
C is for the citizens that we have to be.
A is for ambitions that belong to you and me.

Jennifer B., Grade 8, Covington, Virginia

Cori J., Grade 8, Battle Ground, Washington

America the Beautiful

Nicole C., Grade 8, Battle Ground, Washington

I am proud to be an American kid because of these simple things: Red autumn leaves, majestic mountains. White winter snow and glistening pine trees. Blue summer skies, foaming oceans. Freedom, the color of my country. America, the land where I live.

Dave D., Grade 6, Saugerties, New York

I'm proud to be an American kid because just look around— it's so beautiful! There are so many colors and everybody has a different face and different lives. And I realize it's just a really beautiful place to live!

Sarah S., Kindergarten, Altoona, Pennsylvania

I'm proud to be an American kid because I live in the most beautiful country of all. I love the mountains, the prairies, the beaches, and the plains. It inspires so many young people to be the best. I love my free country.

Megan T., Grade 5, Jackson, Mississippi

To see the flag wave in the air with its fifty stars and thirteen stripes, representing America's states.
To see people donate their time and money to help others.
To see how we have changed since September 11.
They are all beautiful sights that make America wonderful.

Jaclyn E., Grade 6, Rocky Hill, Connecticut

I'm proud to be an American kid because there are beautiful city lights that you can see from the high mountaintops. If you stand in a cornfield and listen hard enough, you can hear the corn growing. You can play while people ride by on horses and cars go fast over the beautiful bridges. I love the song of the birds that sit outside my window. At night when I'm on the porch the song of the crickets and grasshoppers is beautiful to my ears. That's the reason I love America, my home, sweet home.

Ali S., Grade 4, Greeley, Colorado

I'm proud to be an American kid because America is adventurous. We have mountains to climb and forests to hike through. We also have rapids for white-water rafting.

Gavin W., Grade 3, Cheboygan, Michigan

Elana S., Grade 7, Bayside, New York

7

Give Three Cheers for the Red, White, and Blue

I am proud to be an American kid because I like saying the Pledge of Allegiance. It has the word "God" in it, which is my favorite thing about it. "Indivisible" is my favorite word to say because it is a tongue twister and is tricky to say. It means America will never break up your family. "Liberty" means freedom, goodwill, and strength. "Justice" means we will always win as a team for America.

Michael R., Grade 2, East Stroudsburg, Pennsylvania

I'm proud to be an American kid because our flag shows how brave we are.

Taylor G., Kindergarten, Grandview, Missouri

I'm proud to be an American kid because I have always respected the American flag. I am also proud because I say the Pledge of Allegiance five times a week, except for summer.

David P., Grade 4, Gwinn, Michigan

Maxwell K., Grade 5, Lincoln, Rhode Island

Tiffany F., Grade 5, Willow Hill, Pennsylvania

When I see the American flag standing proudly, it reminds me of what our country went through to be what it is today. The red reminds me of the blood shed by soldiers who fought for our country and for freedom. The blue reminds me of the sky and now the sky is our limit. The white reminds me of the stars, and because I live in a country like America, I can reach for the stars!

Meghan L., Grade 8, Webster, New York

I'm proud to be an American kid because of what a particular symbol tells us all. It flutters gently in the wind, bringing happiness to all that watch it wave at them. It brings stars together as its stripes bind our nation as one. Its colors are different, representing all our differences. This symbol is our flag, the flag of the U.S.A. It keeps us standing, standing tall. This flag inspires all that keep it close at heart.

Michelle S., Grade 7, Newington, Connecticut

I love living in the land of the free and the home of the brave. The flag is not just fabric—it's a symbol that everyone in America respects. I show my American pride by respecting our flag and by wearing the colors of the flag on my clothes. I recite the Pledge of Allegiance every day at school, and I admire the men and women who defend our country.

Kim M., Grade 5, Churubusco, Indiana

American Friends and Families

Pricilla S., Grade 3, Milwaukee, Wisconsin

I'm proud to be an American kid because I like American food like Grandma Bea's fried chicken, corn-on-the-cob, and biscuits and gravy. I love to play basketball with my mama or daddy and my little brother. Grammie and I can watch shooting stars in a meteor shower. I feel lucky to have a good family that loves me—just an American kid.

Will Y., Grade 3, Saluda, South Carolina

I'm proud to be an American kid because I have a mother, a father, brothers, and sisters who love me. I have good parents who teach me right from wrong, who give me food when I'm hungry, and who take care of me when I'm sick.

Adriana L., Grade 4, Glenwood, Illinois

I'm proud to be an American kid because I can pet my dog Champ and be with my family, even my grandma.

Trent H., Kindergarten, Aloha, Oregon

I am proud to be an American kid because I am free to have the friends I want to have.

Tyler V., Grade 1, Greenville, North Carolina

I am proud to be an American kid because here in Hawaii you are welcomed in as a member of our huge "ohana," or family. It doesn't matter what color you are, how you worship, or what you believe, because you are still family. No other country in the world opens its doors and hearts to everyone like we do.

Kiau F., Grade 8, Honolulu, Hawaii

I'm proud to be an American kid because I can work with my dad.

Louis V., Kindergarten, Buena, New Jersey

I am proud to be an American kid because I am free and I have a nice family. I have food to eat and friends and a hug and kiss at night. Most of all, I have a dog.

Victoria H., Grade 2, Baton Rouge, Louisiana

I'm proud to be an American kid because I love my family and I love my friends. I love my mom, dad, grannies, sisters, and my cousins. I'm so thankful to be alive and to have a great family and wonderful friends.

Amanda S., Grade 6, McMinnville, Tennessee

Angela F., Grade 4, Erie, Pennsylvania

American Songs and Celebrations

I am proud to be an American kid because every morning after we say the Pledge of Allegiance, we sing a song about America. I like singing songs about America. My favorite is "Yankee Doodle." Being an American is great and fun.

Karlee B., Grade 4, Ontario, California

I'm proud to be an American kid because we have patriotic songs to sing. My favorite song is "God Bless America." I like this song because it says "land that I love."

John S., Grade 4, Northumberland, Pennsylvania

I'm proud to be an American because of Thanksgiving. Thanksgiving is a special time to be with your family. I enjoy spending time with my entire family on Thanksgiving, and having a feast with turkey and ham. It's great to visit and play with my cousins. On Thanksgiving, we give thanks for all the blessings we have in this beautiful country. Thanksgiving is an American tradition, and a wonderful time to celebrate what it means to be an American kid.

Tiffany W., Grade 6, Tampa, Florida

Christalyn L., Grade 2, San Francisco, California

You know you are content when you feel goose bumps on your body when you hear the national anthem, the song that represents our country and its freedom. Nothing can beat that feeling. I am proud to be an American kid!

Sarah L., Grade 8, Cypress, California

I am proud to be an American kid because we have holidays that display American pride. Fourth of July has American pride because we signed the Declaration of Independence on that day in 1776 and we celebrate it every year. We also have Veterans Day because veterans fought for our freedom in many wars. We do activities in school to honor the men and women who fought for our freedom. We also remember all the wars and bad things that have happened in America and remember that we still live in a free country on Memorial Day.

Devin C., Grade 4, West Seneca, New York

Have you ever just been sitting on the ground watching the fireworks and felt that warm, cozy feeling inside you? That feeling is why I am proud to be an American.

Bridgette A., Grade 6, Clarksville, Indiana

Nicole F., Grade 2, East Stroudsburg, Pennsylvania

"Give Me Your Tired, Your Poor..."

Judith A., Grade 5, Grand Island, North Carolina

I am proud to be an American kid because people come here from other countries to be free of dictators and poverty. They come with hopes, dreams, and expectations to a land where everyone is free and can do what makes them happy. These people are now, and forever will be, American citizens. Our country is great because of its diverse culture from all the people from other countries who come and teach us about their culture and heritage.

Katie G., Grade 8, Battle Ground, Washington

I think everyone who comes here makes this country a better place. Everyone should live in America. Everyone come live in the U.S.A.!

Andrew A., Grade 4, Gibsonburg, Ohio

I am proud to be me because I am an American boy. My family is from Mexico but we are proud to be American.

Jesus C., Grade 2, Arlington, Texas

Brianne R., Grade 7, Bayside, New York

I am proud to be an American kid because of how accepting this country is. When my parents were young and my father was in the Vietnam War, he tried to escape to France and other countries. They wouldn't let him in. Only the United States of America let my parents in. My family and I thank America for accepting immigrants from all over the world.

Elmer P., Grade 8, Fort Worth, Texas

America has many different nationalities. My grandparents came here from Italy. They arrived in 1958 by boat. They did not know how to speak English. They left their families, friends, and country behind. I am proud to be an American because America gave my grandparents a better life.

Matthew C., Grade 4, Bayside, New York

I'm proud to be an American kid because people from different countries come here. They come to live, and to get a job, and for peace and freedom. I have friends that are Mexican, Palestinian, Puerto Rican, African American, and Native American. They are what make it fun to be an American kid!

Daniela C., Grade 3, Milwaukee, Wisconsin

Coming to America

Meredith P., Grade 2, Staten Island, New York

I'm proud to be an American kid because in Mexico I didn't have a good house or a good school. Now I have a great house and can get a great education. I'm proud because my mom and dad are free and my sister can get more toys here than in Mexico. Also my dad has better work than in Mexico. I'm proud because President Bush has let me stay in the U.S.A. All in all I am proud to be an American kid in a beautiful state with freedom, joy, and love.

Mariel F., Grade 6, Springdale, Arkansas

I'm proud to be an American kid because I am free to worship my country. I was born in Ecuador but America is my home. I like America because in the country it is nice and warm. You can see cows and horses eating hay and grass. I am also proud to be able to go to school. I love my country. I am proud to be an American thanks to George Washington.

Marcus R., Grade 2, San Jose, California

I am proud to be an American kid because this country gave my family a home away from their home back in Turkey. This country helped my family succeed in life and gave them a place to be free. I'm proud to be able to look up into the sky and see the beautiful red, white, and blue colors. I'm proud to say that America gave me a home, freedom, and most of all, my life!

Belkis G., Grade 8, Lincolnwood, Illinois

I am proud to be an American kid because back in China, everyone dreamt of going to America, home of places like Disney World. But though we imagined seeing such things, we never really believed we could. Only the luckiest got to move to America, and though we tried, none of us really believed we could ever set foot on American ground. Disney World felt like a myth. Then my parents made it. We were going to the U.S. My friends said I was the luckiest kid in the world. They were right.

NanNan L., Grade 6, Salt Lake City, Utah

I'm proud to be an American kid because I'm free to be whatever I want. Nobody takes advantage of me because I'm Vietnamese. I'm a girl in a school where people treat me the same way they treat their family members. I love this country because of the peace and friendship people have with each other. This is the best country in the world.

Jackie M., Grade 7, Tampa, Florida

I'm proud to be an American kid because I have friends of different religions and I can learn about different cultures. People can also learn about me because I am an Asian American from Pakistan. America is the place I like to be.

Hiba H., Grade 5, Elberton, Georgia

We'll Always Remember

Morgan M., Grade 5, Bayside, New York

Some people said the United States would never be the same. That we would never survive. Now, one year later, most of the people's predictions have been proven wrong. Who proved all of those theories wrong? Children, teenagers, adults, and you. The purpose of 9/11 was to tear US apart. It brought strangers, friends, and family closer together. I am only 13, and I have witnessed something truly extraordinary. I was born in 1989, but I became an American on 9/11/01.

Caitlin W., Grade 8, Peoria, Arizona

Resilience is defined as the ability to recover quickly from an illness, change, or misfortune. I think after 9/11 you could easily add America to that definition. I think that's something to be proud of. And I am very proud. God bless the U.S.!

Kyrene G., Grade 6, Salt Lake City, Utah

When two buildings fell apart, fifty states came together.

Michelle S., Grade 8, Berkeley Heights, New Jersey

I'm proud to be an American kid because when there is a problem we stick up for each other, protect each other, and come closer together to solve the conflict. Remember the September 11 tragedy? The attackers expected us to fall apart. Instead we came together, held our flag high, and did not forget our number one reason for living in America: freedom. The brave passengers of Flight 93 tried their hardest to swallow their fears and bring the hijackers off course. Although they lost their lives, they saved many other innocent people. By working together America has shown that we truly cannot be beaten.

Elise M., Grade 7, Doylestown, Pennsylvania

I am proud to be an American kid because I love America. Every night when I say my prayers I say, "God bless the New York people." Sometimes I wish the whole world could be America. I wonder what it is like to be outside America?

Meghan S., Grade 3, Arlington, TX

Lauren P., Grade 6, Plainview, New York

I'm proud to be an American kid because I'm so proud of our country right now. Since September 11, people have been very quiet and mournful. Even though we've lost the people we love, we shouldn't dwell on their deaths. We should celebrate their lives. We have not lost anyone. We have only gained thousands of angels.

Lindsey Jo B., Grade 6, Wexford, Pennsylvania

19

American Patriotism

Mahina H., Grade 5, Pearl City, Hawaii

Patriotism isn't just flags and songs as some countries seem to believe. It's what's inside a person's heart and mind. Patriotism in America is helping others in need. It's donating money to a needy organization. It's reaching out for someone's hand and touching his heart. It's adopting an orphan child. It's loving your neighbor as you love yourself. Patriotism is tons of good things and good deeds. I'm proud to be an American kid because America is truly a patriotic country.

Michelle V., Grade 8, Chesnee, South Carolina

There are many ways I can show my pride in America. Being a good citizen and visiting a memorial for people who died for this country are two examples. Following laws, being respectful to law officers, and picking up trash on the side of the road are ways to be a good citizen. I can also show my pride by visiting a memorial. This won't take very much time, but will show your pride—and our heroes deserve it.

Anna C., Grade 7, Rogers, Arkansas

To me patriotism means the enthusiastic support and love many people have given to the United States. In World War I and World War II many people died for our country's freedom. On December 7, 1941, Japan bombed Hawaii and many innocent people died. On September 11, 2001, Osama Bin Laden attacked the Twin Towers in New York City and killed many innocent people. Most Americans remember all the people who died for our country's freedom, and we honor those people.

Lysette B., Grade 7, Del Rio, Texas

I'm proud to be an American kid and I express that by being in the color guard at my Cub Scout meetings, which means I post the American flag. I also have an American flag on the back of my basketball pole and have lots of eagle statues and carvings all around my house. I say the Pledge of Allegiance every day and sing a patriotic song as a follow-up.

Ben F., Grade 5, Sterling, Illinois

People in America can show they are proud by putting flags on their cars, on their lawns, and on their houses. You can also help people by volunteering and donating things to different places. I put an American flag sticker on my bedroom window. I helped take care of my neighbor's dogs. I washed my mom's car three times inside and out without pay. I did all my homework, and helped my mom around the house.

Jessica F., Grade 5, Redondo Beach, California

I'm proud to be an American kid because we show that we love our country by shooting fireworks, singing patriotic songs, taking care of our country, and wearing red, white, and blue. We say the Pledge of Allegiance every day. We show that we love our country by waving flags. We always treat our country with respect. I love my country, America.

Angelica Beatrice F., Grade 5, Hemingway, South Carolina

It's the Little Things That Count

Haley C., Grade 5, Monroe, Georgia

I am proud to be an American kid because I am free to ride on roller coasters!

Nicholas C., Kindergarten, Copperas Cove, Texas

I'm proud to be an American kid because I love pickles, and in America I can go to the store and buy them whenever I want—except when I have no money. I love pickles so much that I would do almost anything for them, just like I would do almost anything for my country.

Kiara M., Grade 8, Reidsville, Georgia

I'm proud to be an American kid because we get to play sports like baseball, soccer, and golf. I am also proud to be an American because we have hunting and fishing.

Tony D., Grade 3, Soldotna, Alaska

I'm proud to be an American kid because I have the privilege of being able to have music in my life. Not all children can have a big stereo and many CDs in other parts of the world. Music is something I live for. And yet for some children it is something they can't hear or have.

Diana D., Grade 6, Fayetteville, Georgia

I am proud to be an American kid because I get to go to parks and see butterflies. I can study butterflies at my school. I can catch ladybugs and let them free, just like me!

Gabriel G., Grade 1, Alamogordo, New Mexico

I am proud to be an American kid because we have the freedom to dance. We can tap dance with metal shoes, ballet dance with colorful clothes, or dance how we want, like hip-hop, country, or solo.

LaQuasia W., Grade 4, Rice, Texas

In some foreign countries children and adults aren't educated or allowed to read books. If I weren't allowed to read books my life would be boring. Reading and learning is what makes life incredible and exciting. Being an American is wonderful, amazing, and exciting.

Qiana H., Grade 5, Laie, Hawaii

I'm glad that I'm an American because here in America I have the freedom to feed, love, and care for a pet. You might not think that's a big deal, but in other third-world countries children can barely feed themselves, never mind a pet! Just imagine coming to America for the first time and walking into a place called a "supermarket," and finding a whole entire aisle devoted to cat and dog food!

Nicole T., Grade 6, Coventry, Rhode Island

John Michael G., Grade 1, Indianapolis, Indiana

The Land of Opportunity

I'm proud to be an American kid because I have the freedom and ability to laugh, to take care of my family and friends, to be nice, to be respectful, to be a citizen, to be a helper, and to be a good person.

Ashley A., Grade 3, Brownsville, Texas

I'm proud to be an American kid because of the opportunities given to everyone. In my family my mother has to support my brother and me on her own. We live in a great town with wonderful neighbors. My brother and I do well in school and live in a nice, cozy house. That is why I can say that I am extremely proud to be an American kid.

David W., Grade 8, Berkeley Heights, New Jersey

I am proud to be an American kid because in America I can be anything I want to be. I am going to be a doctor, a cheerleader, and a mom. They are all important.

Mikayla M., Kindergarten, Copperas Cove, Texas

I am proud to be an American kid because of the opportunities given in America. I'm from Ukraine and the reason we moved to America was because of the freedoms, opportunities, and technology. Before 9/11 we never knew how lucky we were to live in a country that has everything. I sometimes hate going to school, but we should remind ourselves of other children all over the world that would do anything to go to school.

Anna K., Grade 7, Doylestown, Pennsylvania

I am from Puerto Rico, which makes me an American citizen. I came to America to get a good education and to play baseball. I'm proud to be an American because America always offers us the opportunity to be a good person. I am going to be part of America's future.

Jose V., Grade 4, Jacksonvile, Florida

I'm proud to be an American kid because I'm free to accomplish my dreams and have the opportunity to succeed. Being an American means having freedom of choice. I can grow up to be whatever I please.

Marcela C., Grade 8, Nogales, Arizona

I am proud to be an American kid because I can have dreams that come true.

Kory C., Pre-K, Cape Coral, Florida

I'm proud to be an American kid because I can grow up to be the president, like George Washington, and have my face on a dollar bill. I'm proud to be an American kid because I can have dreams about being rich, like Bill Gates. I could buy a mansion and leave it hollow, so when you sing inside my house it's like show time at the Apollo Theater.

Marcus G., Grade 8, Portageville, Missouri

American Analogies

Being American is the chance to do amazing things. It's riding down the highway with the windows rolled down and the wind blowing your hair back. Being American is freedom! Our roads may not be paved with gold, but they are paved with love—love for this country!

Ninamarie O., Grade 8, El Paso, Texas

I'm proud to be an American kid because America is a child with determination—if something goes wrong, it just gets right back up and tries again.

Brittney B., Grade 7, Downey, California

I am proud to be an American kid because it feels like being part of a rainbow. Rainbows are united, made up of many colors, and are beautiful.

Christine T., Grade 8, Cypress, California

Sarah K., Grade 2, Redondo Beach, California

This country is like a quilt. It is made up of different colors, shapes, and sizes, all together as one, and is strong and lovable.

Samantha C., Grade 6, Bronx, New York

America is like a supermarket. It carries everything you need. We carry equal rights for all, freedom of speech and education, and we'll even throw in a free right to your own religion! Wow, what a bargain! On aisle two you can find every single race out there from Japanese to Scottish. On aisle three you can find massive waves in California to snowy mountains in Alaska. "Clean up on aisle four!" On aisle four is our government, which has been cleaning up a lot of messes that other countries left. Okay, now to the register. Sorry—even in America nothing is cheap!

Philia P., Grade 8, Cypress, California

Being American is like being cuddled in your favorite blanket by the fire. You will always feel safe and warm.

Sabrina K., Grade 6, Sugar Land, Texas

I'm proud to be an American kid because America is a strong fabric and each person is a thread. Patriotism is the steady hand that sews us all together. Do not let our fabric be cut by evil scissors. Instead, let our fabric grow stronger and let us learn to respect each moment we have in this country.

Ivey B., Grade 6, Meriden, Kansas

I am proud to be an American kid because we never give up. We are just like a turtle stuck on its back that keeps trying to turn itself over. And the people are like a variety of M&M's® in a bag—the different colors represent all the different races.

Sean N., Grade 6, Claymont, Delaware

America's Melting Pot

I'm proud to be an American kid because of all the good food. The food from all the millions of restaurants is almost as good as my grandma's cooking. Pizza, pancakes, and burgers, oh my! There is also a great variety among the foods. On the West Coast you can find a lot of Oriental food. I may be wrong, but I think you can find any food you want in the United States, even Dutch food!

Bruno K., Grade 7, Splendora, Texas

I'm proud to be an American kid because there is a rainbow of many children.

Sunshine H., Grade 1, Wauwatosa, Wisconsin

I'm proud to be an American kid because I have learned about how great our country is from the kids around me. I attend a school with children from many countries. Their families came here for freedom and better opportunities. They want a better education, good jobs, better housing, enough food to eat, and the chance to practice their religion and beliefs. I have learned about my schoolmates' lives which were sometimes hard in their countries. Together we learn about America. Being with these kids at school makes me realize why I am proud to be an American kid.

Maddie B., Grade 3, Columbia, Maryland

I'm proud to be an American kid because I am part of a group of people and cultures from around the world, living together with freedom and liberty.

Elidh B., Grade 3, St. Thomas, U.S. Virgin Islands

Amanda F., Grade 6, Columbia, Missouri

I'm proud to be an American kid because America is made up of so many different people. No two people are exactly alike. Everyone has different backgrounds, personalities, and cultures. Everyone has different interests, opinions, values, and ideas. America is one big melting pot. Everyone gets to be the way they want to be and act the way they want to act. In this country it's okay to be different. But the thing that makes me most proud is that despite our differences, we can pull together in time of crisis to be one.

Angela R., Grade 7, Greentown, Pennsylvania

I am proud to be an American kid because of the diversity of our nation. As I look around my classrooms, I see Chinese, Russian, English, and Spanish students. There are kids in wheelchairs, kids with hearing aids, and kids struggling with Down's Syndrome. There are Muslim, Jewish, and Christian children. No one is the same. This is true for the rest of the United States. Every day immigrants enter this country, bringing new ideas. Every day America benefits from the contributions of so many different cultures.

Caitlin D., Grade 8, Naperville, Illinois

Free to Be Me

I was given the best prize of all—being born an American! Being born knowing that I can have a dream and then go after it. Being born knowing that I can walk outside without being interrogated. Being born knowing that I can have friends of different races and religions and be okay with it. Most of all, being born knowing that I can have freedom. It might not seem like much to you, but I'm honored to call myself an American!

Aaron P., Grade 6, Vineland, New Jersey

I'm proud to be an American kid because I love all the goodies that come from being a citizen of this country. My inner spirit and mind are free to follow any path. I do not have to place my feet in another person's footprints. I'm able to wear whatever I believe looks good on me or makes me feel special. I can express my thoughts through writing, speaking, or drawing. My dreams never have to be just dreams because in America nothing is impossible.

Regina W., Grade 3, Sterling Heights, Michigan

I'm proud to be an American kid because I can choose who I marry and how many kids I want.

Victoria W., Kindergarten, Grandview, Missouri

I am proud to be an American kid because I don't have to worry about keeping my comments to myself. In America freedom of speech means kids and adults can make a difference with just a few brief words. You may not think that words can make a lasting impression, but just think about Todd Beamer and his phrase, "Let's roll!"

Christy M., Grade 7, Splendora, Texas

'm proud to be an American kid because I'm free to do things as long as my mommy and daddy and the law say so. f I want to do something, my mommy doesn't have to go on he telephone and call the president and ask his permission.

Gregory R., Grade 3, Glen Rock, New Jersey

'm proud to be an American kid because I can shout from he highest mountain or whisper any thought in my friend's ear because I have the freedom to speak what's on my mind. My hair can be long, short, spiked, or striped, and I can wear polka dots with stars because I have the right to express myself. Being a kid in America means I can be an ndividual—not just a copy of someone else.

Kevin M., Grade 3, Port Huron, Michigan

'm proud to be an American kid because I can play outside and not be afraid.

Chase W., Grade 2, Brookings, South Dakota

'm proud to be an American kid because I am free to do vhat I want with my mom's permission.

Marguette M., Grade 3, New Castle, Pennsylvania

'm proud to be an American kid because I can go to school at home. I can live in a nice, safe home with room to play.

Bryce and Ethan G., Pre–K and Kindergarten,
Lubbock, Texas

The Home of the Brave— American Heroes

I'm proud to be an American kid because I come from the same country as many heroes. It makes me proud knowing the 9/11 heroes, our people overseas, President George W. Bush, former New York Mayor Rudy Giuliani, the nine miners in Pennsylvania, and many others are from the same country as me.

Briana W., Grade 7, Greentown, Pennsylvania

I'm proud to be an American kid because our country is protected by a lot of proud Americans who are defending us and willing to give away their lives to save our country.

Jennica M., Grade 6, Friendship, Maine

I am proud of the young men and women who fought for this country to give me freedom. When I turn 18 and my country needs me to fight for our freedom I would be honored to fight for the U.S.A. and keep our freedom alive.

Michael S., Grade 6, Palm Harbor, Florida

Michael F., Pre-K, Ft. Stewart, Florida

am proud to be an American because the firemen put the ires out and the police catch the bad guys.

Dylan Jacob H., Grade 2, San Clemente, California

'm proud to be an American kid because we have had a lot f leaders in our country, such as Harriet Tubman, Rosa arks, Martin Luther King, Jr., and Sojourner Truth, who nake our country shine. They were very brave people. It's eople like them who inspire me and make me want to do omething with my life.

Delky K., Grade 7, New Orleans, Louisiana

am proud to be an American kid because our president is tanding strong and not letting us get pushed around.

Melissa L., Grade 5, Fort Wayne, Indiana

am proud to be an American kid because I'm honored to ve in a nation where you can enjoy the freedom that our orefathers fought so hard to achieve.

Robert M., Grade 8, Lyndhurst, New Jersey

m proud to be an American kid because I have a grandpa who ught for our country in World War II. He was stationed in the hilippine Islands. I'm proud of my grandpa for being so brave hen he could have been killed.

Kristina C., Grade 4, Port Byron, New York

m proud to be an American kid because of our country's iilitary. America's military is ready to defend our country ith a moment's notice, just like the Minutemen. It has efended our country in many wars. If it weren't for those rave men and women who fought and died for freedom, we ould not be here.

Dominic A., Grade 7, Westfield, Massachusetts

A+ Education

I'm proud to be an American kid because I love my schoo'

Daymon H., Kindergarten, Rentz, Georgi.

I am proud to be an American kid because I can get a education from good schools and learn to read. When read, I can explore the world. I am able to learn everything That way, I will grow up to be a healthy and strong America kid.

Safraz H., Grade 2, Brooklyn, New Yor

I'm proud to be an American kid because I can get a goo education. I can learn to read, do mathematics, spell, stud science and English, and learn about my country.

Zachary W., Grade 5, Tripoli, Iow

I'm proud to be an American kid because I go to a grea school.

Nicole E., Grade 1, St. Louis, Missou

'm proud to be an American kid because I have teachers who care. They just don't give up on me when I don't get things as fast as other kids. They make sure I understand. They try to be good role models.

Kayla D., Grade 4, Brooklyn, New York

'm proud to be an American kid because we have very good schools and teachers, and if we did not have good schools or teachers we would not be able to learn about America.

Staci H., Grade 7, Caddo Mills, Texas

'm proud to be an American kid because I have opportunities, such as getting an excellent education. Sometimes we take education for granted, especially being a kid. In some countries kids have to grow up very fast. They grow up worrying about survival, about wars on their doorsteps, while in America we are able to be kids, looking forward to a bright future.

Michaela H., Grade 6, Yakima, Washington

'm proud to be an American kid because my parents support me with school. After school I stay home and do my homework—I don't have to work hard to earn money like many kids whom I saw in Vietnam. At school my teacher shows me how to be a good person. I respect my teacher and do what she teaches me. Every day I go home to do all my homework to get good grades. And when it is time to go to class I make sure to pack to be on time. When I grow up I want to become a teacher and convince kids to do better and listen to their parents and teachers.

Jimmy L., Grade 3, Jersey City, New Jersey

I am proud to be an American kid because I am free to do my homework!

John G., Grade 1, Alamogordo, New Mexico

"One Nation, Under God...

Audrey B., Grade 1, St. Louis, Missouri

I am proud to be an American because I am free to worship God. Our Pledge of Allegiance is very thoughtful. I think "one nation under God" means that God is watching us and helping us through difficult times.

Ryan D., Grade 4, Escondido, California

I'm proud to be an American kid because I read the Bible and I can learn about Jesus in America.

M'Kenzea S., Kindergarten, Bethel, Missouri

I'm proud to be an American kid because I have the right to choose my own religion and no one can tell me otherwise. In some other countries people might not be able to choose their own religion and that's wrong. Religion should be personal choice.

Deanne M., Grade 7, Battle Ground, Washington

Religion is why America started in the first place—the Pilgrims came here from England for religious freedom, so they could worship the god of their choice. I have pride in knowing that I'm American, and that's a great feeling.

Ben D., Grade 6, Coventry, Rhode Island

...with Liberty and Justice for All"

I am proud to be an American kid today because in the old days colored Americans couldn't get on a school bus, go to the same school, or drink from the same water fountain as the white people did. If I want to be someone in life I know I have a chance, regardless of my color. I can earn a degree and become a doctor or a lawyer. I know I have to work hard for what I want and for what I always dream of.

Moises B., Grade 6, Stockton, California

I am proud to be an American kid because we're not judged by our looks. My sister is handicapped and all my friends respect her like they respect me.

Matthew L., Grade 4, Bethesda, Maryland

Being an American is an honor and a blessing. Here, men and women are treated equally. In some other countries, women are excluded from many privileges, such as schooling, holding a job, and voting for their rights. In many regions around the world, women are not allowed to expose their skin. If they neglect to follow this law, they face severe consequences. But in this grand nation, women have careers, lives, and they make a difference.

Sheeba C., Grade 8, Lincolnwood, Illinois

In America, all citizens are equal,
It's such a cool country,
you'd wish there were a sequel!

Amanda B., Grade 8, Naples, Florida

America Cares

I'm proud to be an American kid because we can help people.

Mayra R., Grade 1, Elkhart, Indiana

I'm proud to be an American kid because whenever I fall off my bike or trip and cut myself there is always a person there to give me a hand. My teachers in my school are also really nice to me. Whenever I don't know something they always help me. When I go to the store and buy something and I don't have enough money, a person is kind enough to give me a quarter or fifty cents.

Ryan B., Grade 5, Macomb, Michigan

I am proud to be an American kid because we stand united. When one country is hurt, we try to help. Americans try to help people, even outside of the United States. We collect money for services like UNICEF and Red Cross. We also collect money for local cases like homeless shelters, feeding the poor, and helping the poor and old.

Kerry A., Grade 5, Atlanta, Georgia

Andrea F., Grade 5, Willow Hill, Pennsylvania

I'm proud to be an American kid because America helps others. Nice people donate clothes to help the poor at St. Vincent dePaul, Goodwill, or the Salvation Army. People donate hair for those who have cancer. They send cans or presents to those who can't afford to buy gifts or food. We also send money, medicine, clothes, or food to people in other countries. There are good doctors that try to find a cure for cancer or AIDS. Even though America's not perfect, there are people who try to make it the best it can be.

Angela R., Grade 7, Tucson, Arizona

I'm proud to be an American kid because I know the people who fight for our country are fighting for peace and that's what we need, peace. If we can start in our neighborhood and spread peace there, and if we work hard enough, we can move the peace to our city. As the peace spreads from one city to another, it will finally reach the whole entire state. If we tell states and they tell other states we can make our country peaceful. If we could get our country to be peaceful, people can feel good for themselves.

Travis W., Grade 6, Tucson, Arizona

I'm proud to be an American kid because I help other people when they are hurt. I like to help sad people become happy. I am a proud American when I help my friends. A proud American rocks!

Maranda W., Grade 2, South Park, Pennsylvania

Kristina U., Grade 4, Portland, Connecticut

39

What It Means to Me

John S., Grade 8, Cypress, California

Being an American is more than just living in a country, it is like being that country. We as Americans go through what our country goes through. If there is a tragedy like 9/11 we all suffer—not just the families of those who died. When innocent people die it's like losing part of America. When countries hold our citizens captive they hold part of America captive. They take part of our country away from us.

Elizabeth D., Grade 8, Bureau, Illinois

To be an American means to accept all people and to be accepted along with them. No matter what religion, culture, origin, custom, or any kind of diversity. It means to understand freedom—how it feels, what it is, and what it really means to have it. It means that you're united with every person in the country. It is an incredible, invisible bond that makes the United States what it is today.

Molly M., Grade 6, Columbus, Ohio

I think being an American means being brave, having justice, and caring for one another. An American is someone who is proud. We do heroic things. We help in times of need. We stick up for each other. We do what we have to do. We stand up and speak out. We are united and strong. We are American!

Carly R., Grade 7, Columbus, Ohio

I'm proud to be an American kid because being born in America is the best thing that could happen to a kid! The last four letters in American spell "I can." That means I can do anything I set my mind to do!

Michelle B., Grade 4, Fort Worth, Texas

I'm proud to be an American kid because I live on a beautiful island that has been blessed with the freedom to choose without losing its true identity.

Pride is dignity and a sense of value that doesn't have to be displayed for all to see. It's also the greatness I feel inside when I listen to the national anthem. It's that sense of dignity that makes me proud to be an American kid living in Puerto Rico. I know that I'm special because I honor two flags, yet I belong to only one nation.

Lisa M., Grade 9, Hatillo, Puerto Rico

I am proud to be an American kid because of what I represent. I represent freedom, justice, and equal rights for people of all races, genders, and backgrounds. I represent food banks, homeless shelters, and donation programs. I represent firemen, policemen, doctors, lawyers, executives, mothers, fathers, and people who take time out of their day to give a helping hand. When you say I am an American it's more than just that. It has a deeper meaning that is impossible to describe. Next time you talk about being an American, remember what you represent and why you represent it.

Zach Z., Grade 7, Portland, Oregon

Patriotic Poetry

I am not hungry, I am not sad,
I go to church, and I'm rarely mad.
I sleep in a nice and cozy bed,
My mom always kisses my head.
I learn at school and see my friends.
We are so proud to be Americans!

Kristin M., Grade 6, Viola, Arkansas

Brittany C., Grade 5, Churubusco, Indiana

I'm proud to be an American kid,
To defend my country as my fathers did.
I'm free to speak when I'm right,
I'm free to run and free to fight.
I'm free to climb the mountains high,
I'm free to drive in the countryside.
I'm free to laugh and free to sing,
I'm free to do most anything.
I'm free to live and free to cry,
For all the people who have died.
But most of all I'm glad to say,
That I believe the American way.
For all the things my fathers did,
I'm proud to be an American kid!

Trinidad C., Grade 8, Naples, Florida

A tragic thing happened on September 11,
when many good people went to heaven.
This land I love and know so well,
broke apart when the twin towers fell.
It was so sad it made me cry.
Why did all those good people die?
I asked my mom why they did it.
She said, "America's great and they wouldn't admit it."
America the beautiful, with a flag of stripes and stars.
Watch out other countries, victory is ours!

Kasey C., Grade 8, Linthicum, Maryland

Trevor O., Grade 5, Anaheim, California

As an American I'll always be free,
to make my own choices, be different, be me.
I know I am lucky to live in this place,
where we are free to be us, no matter our race.
Even though we're all different, united we stand.
We've all worked together to create this strong land.
The terrorists attacked so our nation would fall,
and even though it was tragic, our country stood tall.
As I watched our great nation and all that it did,
I am so proud to be an American kid.

Carlie B., Grade 8, Tucson, Arizona

Let Freedom Ring

I'm proud to be an American kid because I was born free!

Brandon R., Grade 2, Staten Island, New York

I'm proud to be an American kid because we don't have a king to tell us what to do.

Hannah S., Kindergarten, Foley, Alabama

I'm proud to be an American kid because our country is the finest country I think you will ever find. I think that if you looked one hundred times on the globe you still wouldn't find a country freer than ours. I'm really happy I was born in America and I'm proud of my country, too.

Coleen O., Grade 3, Warminster, Pennsylvania

I'm proud to be an American kid because I can walk outside and go to school without worrying that I'm going to be criticized, or worse yet, arrested because I am different than everyone else is. Here you can be white, black, or even polka-dotted, and everyone respects it.

Tess C., Grade 6, Lampeter, Pennsylvania

Some children only dream of having the great things we have. They might lose their families because of war. People are sometimes split from loved ones, and must live by certain rules because they are not free. I'm glad to be such a lucky, grateful, true American kid.

Erin M., Grade 6, Solomons, Maryland

I am proud to be an American kid because you have freedom and the schools are awesome. I have lived in three other countries—Malaysia, China, and Japan—and have always been proud to be an American. This country is so awesome. I am just so proud to be an American. USA rocks!

Danielle H., Grade 5, Glendale, Arizona

I'm proud to be an American kid because we have freedom of speech. In some countries you can't say anything bad about the leader. In this country you can say that you don't like the president. I personally would not say that because I like Mr. Bush. He makes a great president.

Abigail R., Grade 5, Buzzards Bay, Massachusetts

I'm proud to be an American kid because I know that my country welcomes all the people of the world who have problems in their countries. That means that this country opens its doors, and any person can have freedom of speech or go to church if they want to go.

Mary G., Grade 5, West New York, New Jersey

I'm proud to be an American kid because America is a free country. For example, if you steal from a store, you're free to go to jail.

Stefan M., Grade 5, Collins, Mississippi

You Can Quote Me

Krystle W., Grade 5, Pearl City, Hawaii

In an upside-down world, America always stays right-side up!

Keith C., Grade 3, Opa-Locka, Florida

I'm proud to be an American kid because in America there is always a hero standing next to me.

Holly O., Grade 5, Caledonia, Michigan

To be a kid in America is like being honored with the most important award in the world.

Deannie D., Grade 6, Brooklyn, New York

The day I'm not proud to be an American is the day pigs fly.

Lauren C., Grade 8, Fort Worth, Texas

In America, everyone may look different, but we are all the same.

Joshua P., Grade 4, Tampa, Florida

My love for my country is so great that I wish I could group-hug all of America at once!

Lauren E., Grade 6, Oviedo, Florida

If every country were as free as America, this would be a great world.

Bailey B., Grade 4, Notus, Idaho

I love having America as my country because we are all one big happy family and I think that is the best possible way to run a country.

Stevvi M., Grade 6, APO AP Guam

Be proud that you're an American and don't take it for granted. Some kids would do anything to be in our shoes.

Brittani H., Grade 7, Shepherdville, Kentucky

Since I have come to this country, I have seen lots of different people who live together in peace. When the day comes that I become an American, I will be very proud!

Ivelaw C., Grade 3, Brooklyn, New York

I'm proud to be an American kid because:
* I can get an education
* I can practice any religion
* I can be whatever I want
* I can say whatever I want
* I can go to college
* I can vote democratically
* I can be the president
* I can express my individuality
* I can speak my opinions
* I can show my creativity
* All of the above

Bianca L., Grade 5, Long Beach, California

The overall reason why I'm proud to be an American kid is because I love who I am and without America I could not be me. So thanks, America. I love you.

Cassandra H., Grade 7, Dingmans Ferry, Pennsylvania

Cassandra H., Grade 7, Bayside, New York